Contents

- **UNIT 1** My Backpack 4
- **UNIT 2** It's Me! 6
- **UNIT 3** Clothes are Fun! 8
- **UNIT 4** Happy Birthday! 10
- **UNIT 5** Happy Home 12
- **UNIT 6** Farm Life 14
- **UNIT 7** So Much Food! 16
- **UNIT 8** Let's Go! 18
- My Progress 20
- Cutouts C1
- Stickers S1

The Bebop Band

The Bebop Friends

UNIT 1 — My Backpack

Lesson 1

🎧 **S1** Stick the school objects inside the backpack. Point, say, and count. Sing the song: *Here in My Backpack.*

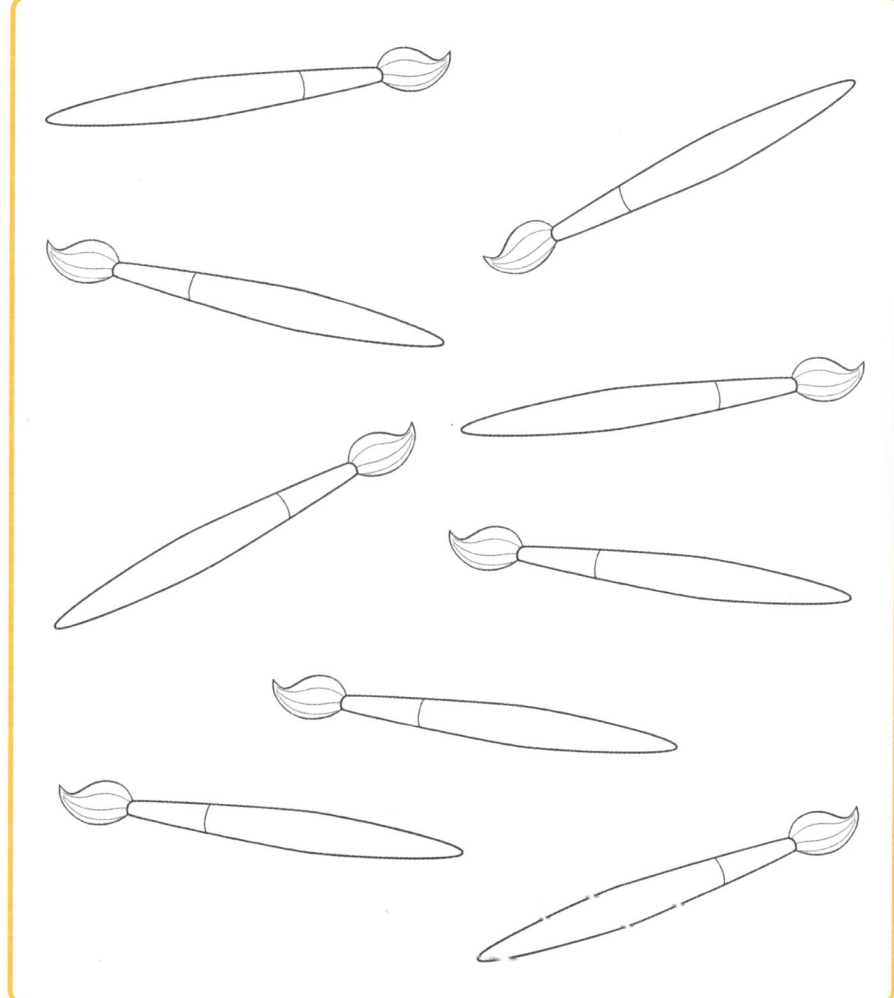

7 8 9 10 11   **7 8 9 10 11**

Count the school objects. Color the group that has less objects with red. Color the group that has more objects with black. Circle the correct number of paintbrushes and pencils.

UNIT 2 — It's Me!

Lesson 1

 **S3** Stick the missing parts on Lucy and Paul's body. Sing the song: *These Parts Make Up Me!*

Lesson 2

Connect the pictures. Do the actions.

UNIT 2

UNIT 3 · Clothes are Fun!

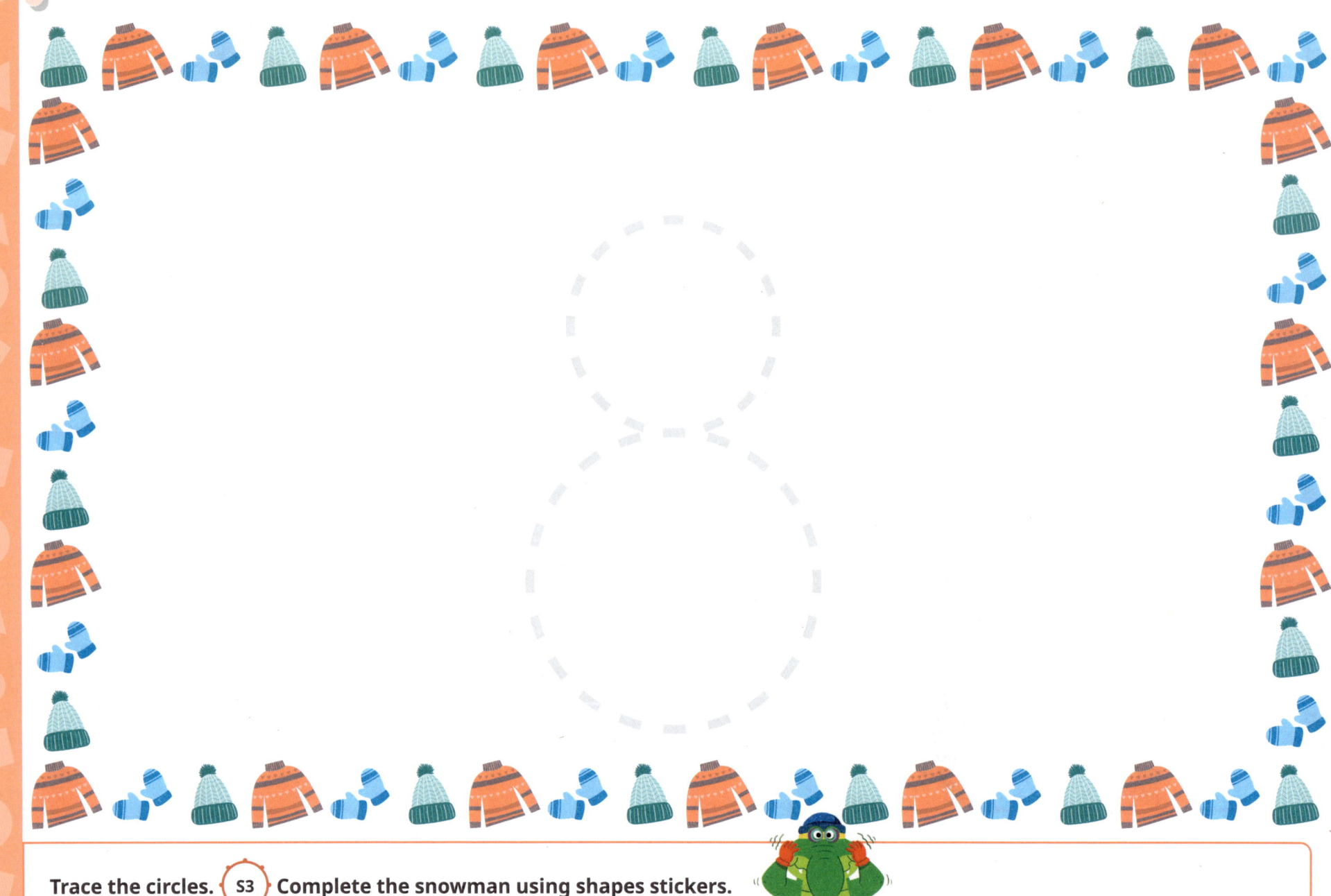

Lesson 1

Trace the circles. (S3) Complete the snowman using shapes stickers.

Lesson 2

 Point and say. Count the clothes. S3 Stick the correct number of clothes in the circles. Sing the song: *I Love My Clothes!*

UNIT 3

UNIT 4 Happy Birthday!

Lesson 1

Circle the ingredients to make a chocolate cake.

Lesson 2

1

2

3

4

 Connect the numbers to the pictures to sequence the steps to make a cake. Sing the song: *It's a Party!*

UNIT 5 Happy Home

Lesson 1

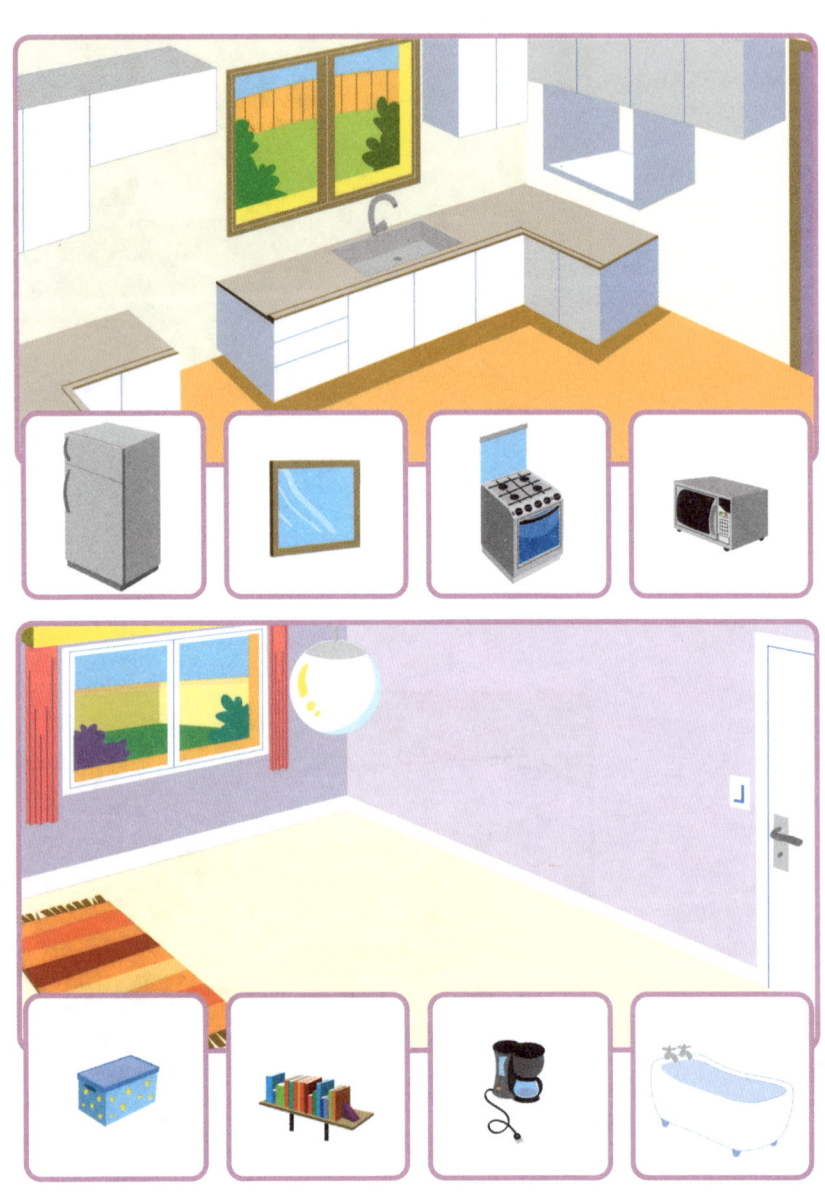

Circle the correct objects from each place.

Unit 8   Cutout

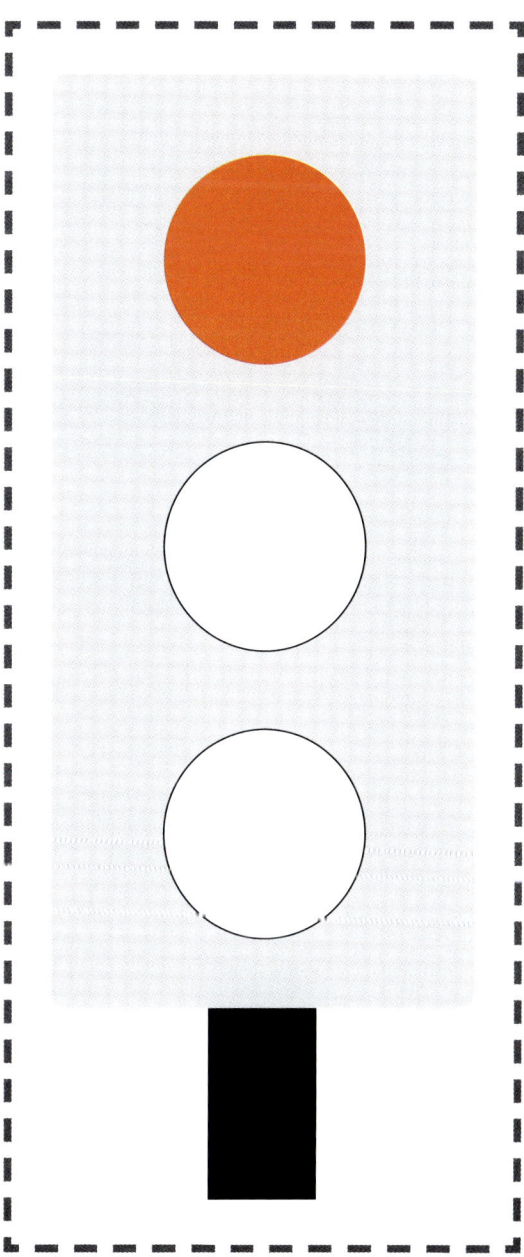

Unit 1 Stickers

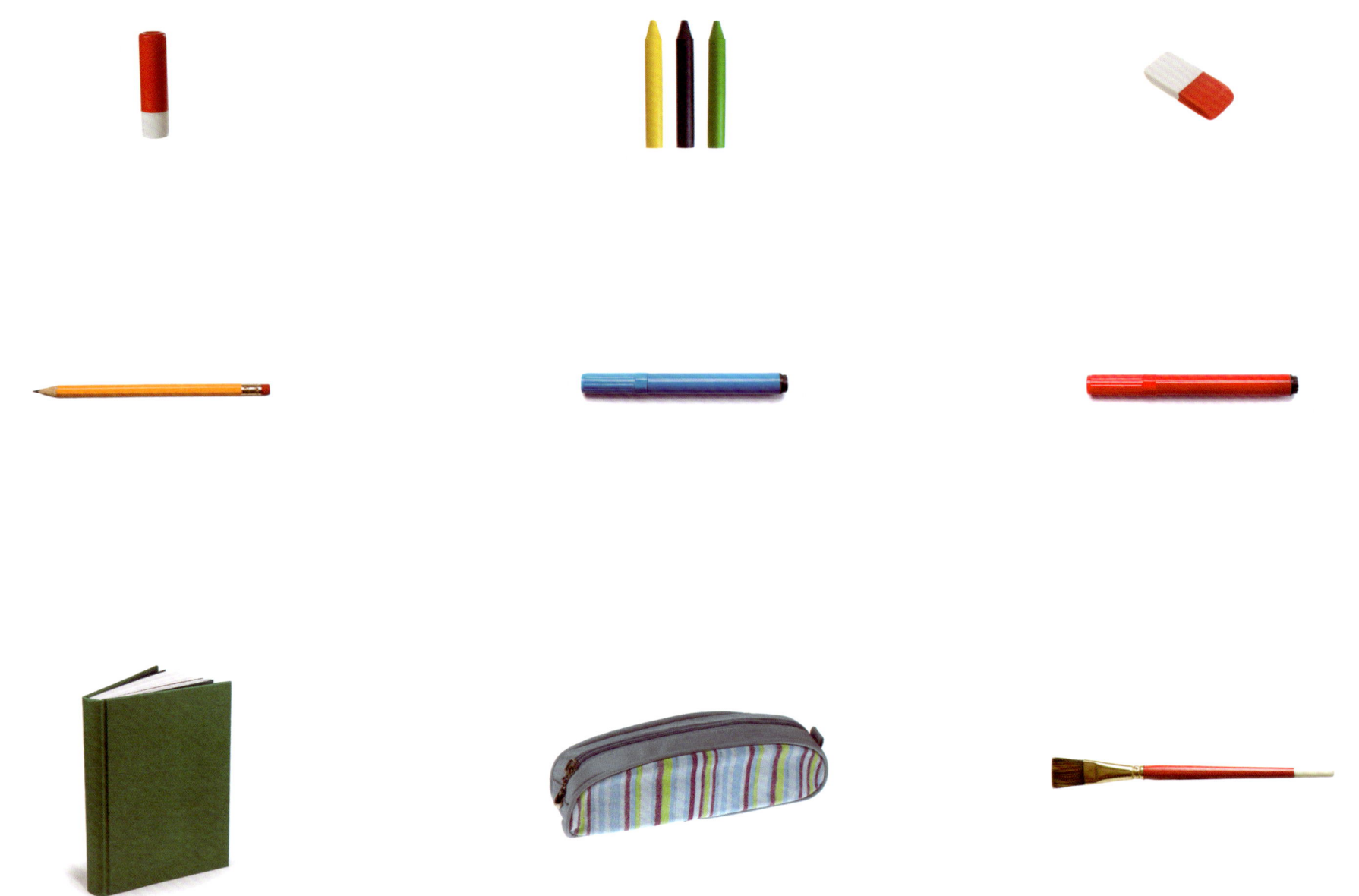

Unit 2 Stickers

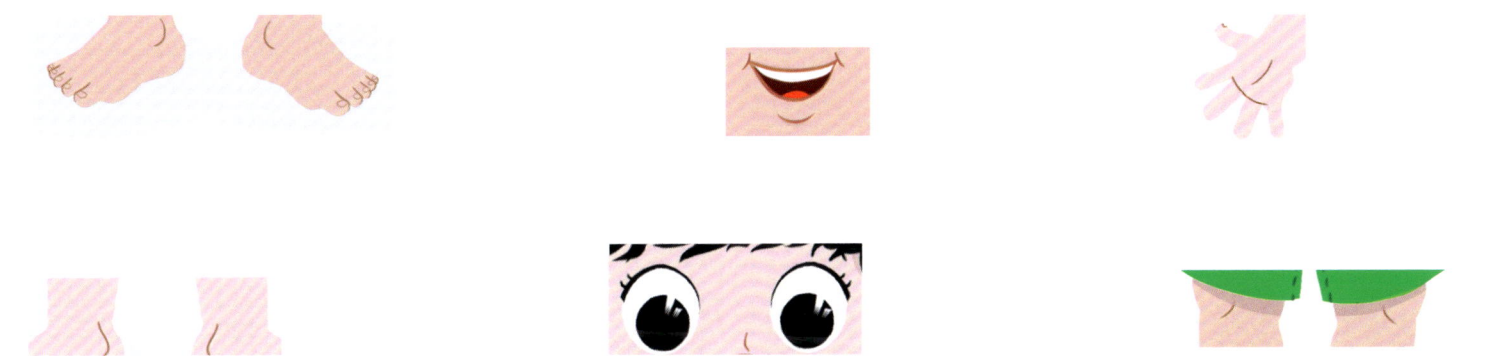

Unit 3 Stickers

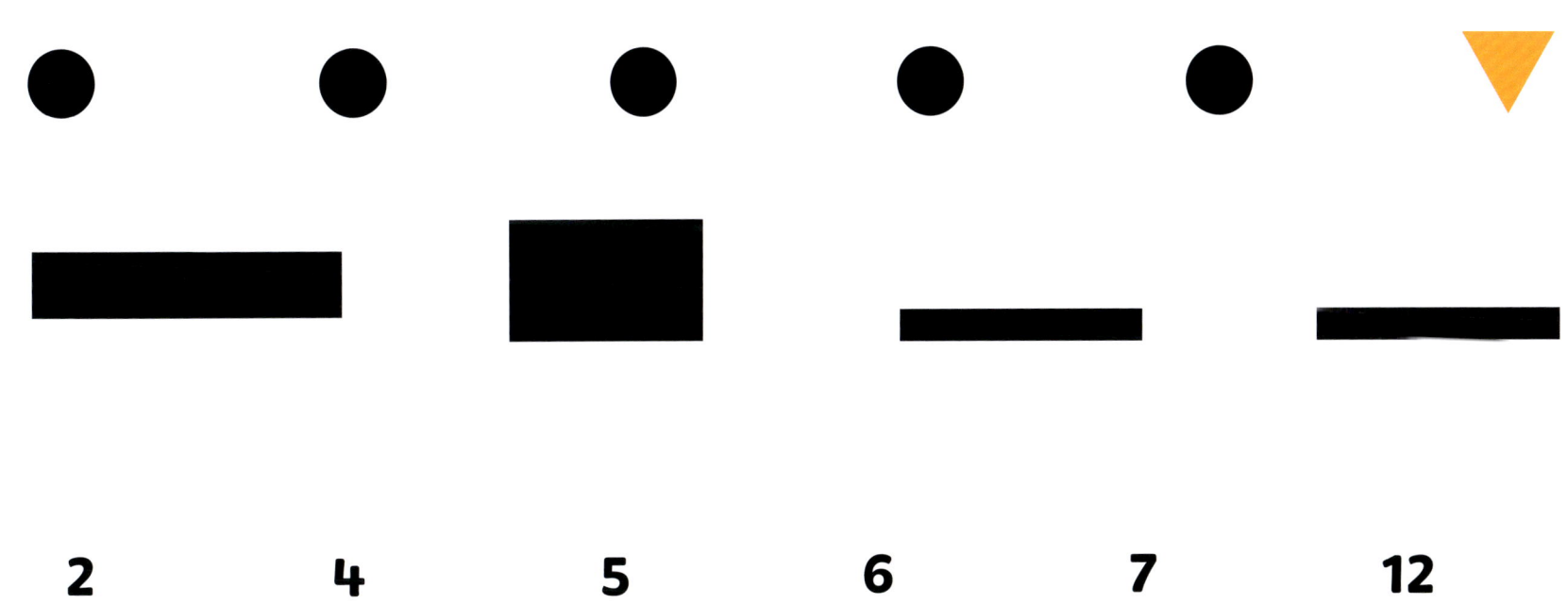

| 2 | 4 | 5 | 6 | 7 | 12 |

Lesson 2

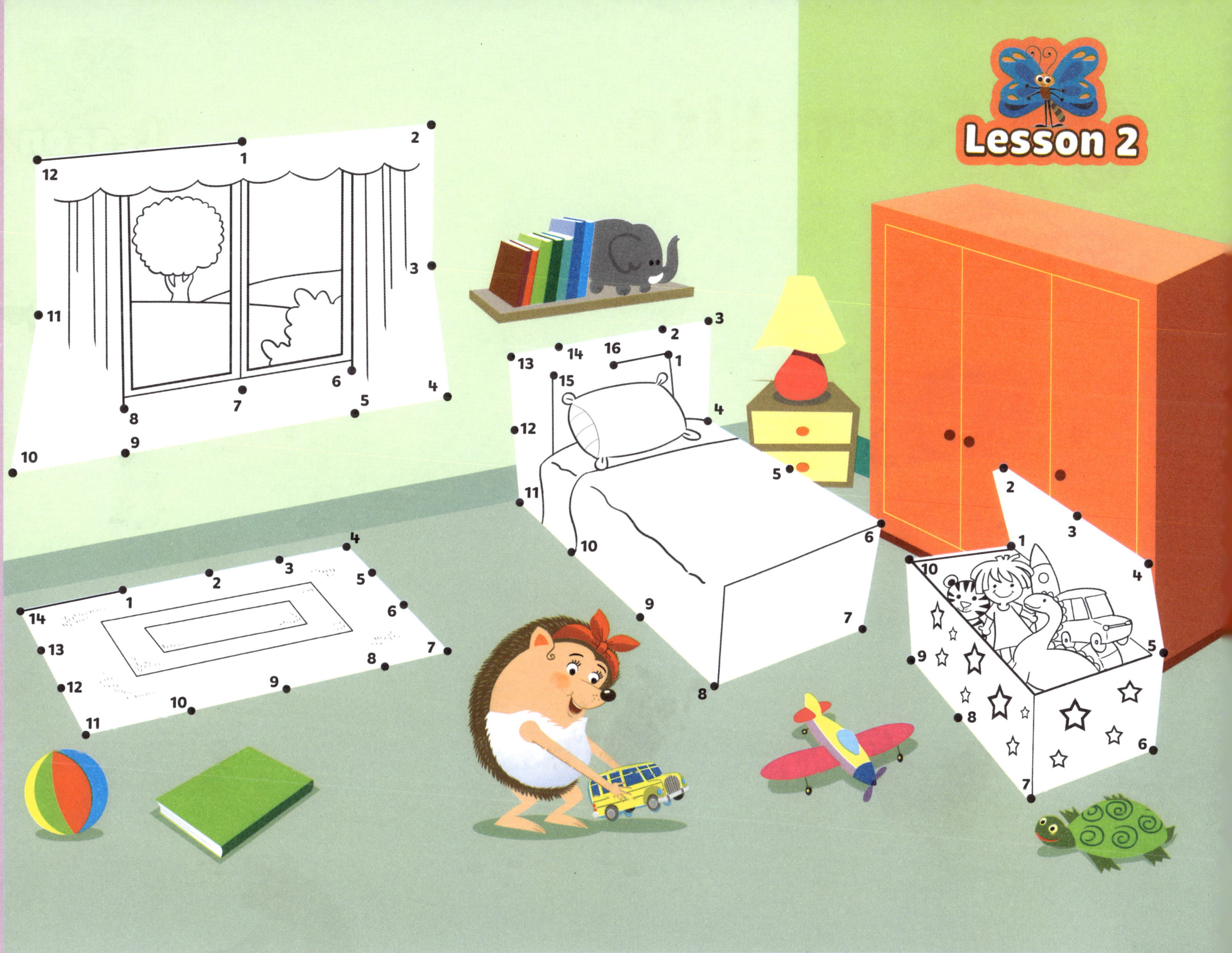

Count and connect the dots to complete the pictures. Color the pictures. Sing the song: *Everything in Its Place!*

UNIT 6 Farm Life

Lesson 1

Listen, point, and say. Circle the baby animals. Sing the song: *Animal Sounds*.

Lesson 2

Connect the correct item that comes from each animal.

UNIT 6

UNIT 7 — So Much Food!

Lesson 1

11 12 13 14 15
16 17 18 19 20

🎧 Listen, point, and say the numbers. Color the numbers 11 to 15 orange. Color the numbers 16 to 20 purple.

Lesson 2

 Circle the pictures with more food in each box. Sing the song: *Yummy Food Here for You!*

UNIT 8 — Let's Go!

Lesson 1

🎧 **Paste green or red paper on the traffic lights. Sing the song:** *Stop and Listen* **and do the actions.**

Lesson 2

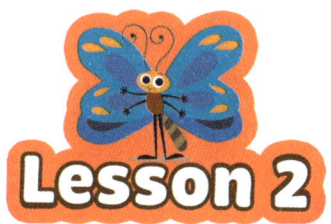

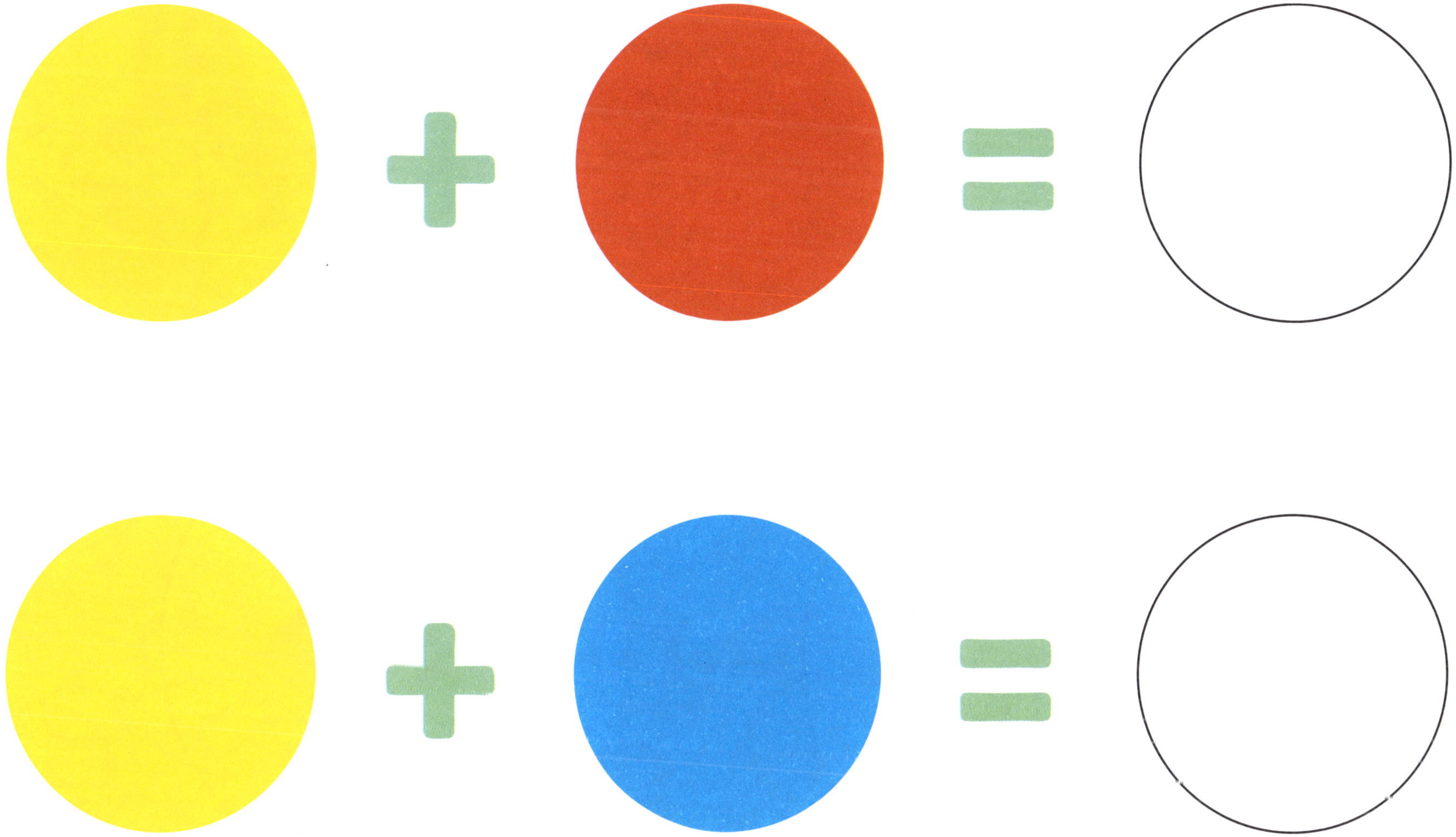

C1 **Mix the colors to complete the traffic light cutout.**

My Progress

Color the number after you complete the unit.

Macmillan Education Limited
4 Crinan Street
London N1 9XW

Companies and representatives throughout the world

Bebop and Friends Level 2 Math and Science Book ISBN 978-1-035-10941-8
Bebop and Friends Level 2 Math and Science Book with Math and Science eBook Pack ISBN 978-1-035-10942-5

Text, design, and illustration © Macmillan Education Limited 2022
Written by Gabriela Duenha Dimitrov

The author has asserted their right to be identified as the author of this work in accordance with the Copyright, Designs and Patents Act 1988.

This edition published 2022
First edition entitled "Bebop" published 2014 by Macmillan Education Limited

All rights reserved. No part of this publication may be reproduced, stored in a retrieval system, transmitted in any form, or by any means, electronic, mechanical, photocopying, recording, or otherwise, without the prior written permission of the publishers.

Design by Macmillan Education Ltd, with contributions by Design Divertido
Page makeup by Figurattiva Editorial
Illustrated by Ilustra Cartoon, Michelle Todd (The Bright Agency) p. 2
Cover design by Macmillan Education Limited
Cover illustration by Ilustra Cartoon

The publishers would like to thank Rich Rafterman, Argila, and Minke Edição e Produção Cultural.

The author and publishers would like to thank the following for permission to reproduce their photographs:

Getty Images/iStockphoto/eliflamra p. 8, Getty Images/iStockphoto/Evgeniya Mukhitova p. 8, Getty Images/iStockphoto/Inna Tanasiienko. 8, Getty Images/iStockphoto/YuanruLi p. 9, Getty Images/iStockphoto/Olga Gillmeister p. 9, Getty Images/iStockphoto/Piotr Polaczyk p. 9, Getty Images/iStockphoto/sergarck p. 9, Getty Images/iStockphoto/demidoffaleks p. 9, Getty Images/iStockphoto/danikancil p. 9, Getty Images/iStockphoto/unalozmen p. 10, Getty Images/iStockphoto/ChViroj p. 10, Getty Images/iStockphoto/Everyday better to do everything you love p. 10, Getty Images/iStockphoto/Pineapple Studio p. 10, Getty Images/iStockphoto/atoss p. 10, Getty Images/iStockphoto/Savany p. 10, Getty Images/iStockphoto/GlobalP p. 14, Getty Images/iStockphoto/Evgeniy1 p. 14, Getty Images/iStockphoto/Antagain p. 14, Getty Images/iStockphoto/ajt p. 15, Getty Images/iStockphoto/asajdler p. 15, Getty Images/iStockphoto/amphotora p. 15, Getty Images/iStockphoto/backhanding p. 15, Getty Images/iStockphoto/Clara Bastian p. 15, Getty Images/iStockphoto/Ornitolog82 p. 15, Getty Images/iStockphoto/DJSrki p. S1, Getty Images/iStockphoto/Tevarak p. S1, Getty Images/iStockphoto/Fotonen p. S1, Getty Images/iStockphoto/t_kimura p. S1, Getty Images/iStockphoto/dlerick p. S1, Getty Images/iStockphoto/Recebin p. S1, Getty Images/iStockphoto/gynane p. S1, Getty Images/iStockphoto/blackred p. S1

These materials may contain links for third party websites. We have no control over, and are not responsible for, the contents of such third party websites. Please use care when accessing them.

The inclusion of any specific companies, commercial products, trade names or otherwise does not constitute or imply its endorsement or recommendation by Macmillan Education Limited.

Printed and bound in Uruguay